STECK-VAUGHN

# Comprehension Skills

# CONTEXT

## LEVEL
## B

Linda Ward Beech
Tara McCarthy
Donna Townsend

STECK-VAUGHN
C O M P A N Y
A Subsidiary of National Education Corporation

| | |
|---|---|
| *Executive Editor:* | Diane Sharpe |
| *Project Editor:* | Melinda Veatch |
| *Senior Editor:* | Anne Rose Souby |
| *Design Coordinator:* | Sharon Golden |
| *Project Design:* | Howard Adkins Communications |
| *Cover Illustration:* | Rhonda Childress |
| *Photographs:* | Texas Department of Highways (wheat) |
| | Scott Huber (bread) |

ISBN 0-8114-7833-5

5 6 7 8 9 10 VP 02 01 00 99 98 97

Using context is a way to learn new words. In this book you will learn how to use context.

What is context? Look at the picture. What do you think of when you say *wheat*? Do you think of golden fields or a loaf of bread? The picture shows wheat in two different *contexts*.

# *What Is Context?*

You can use context to learn new words. If you find a word you do not know, look at the words around it. These other words can help you guess what the word means.

Look at the words below. Choose a word and write it on the line.

Night and _____

Did you write *day*? Why did you write that word? Some words go together. *Day* goes with *night*. The context helped you choose the right word.

## *Try It!*

Read the story below. It has a word you may not know. The word is printed in **dark letters**. See if you can find out what the new word means.

◆

**Chuck Berry Makes a Hit**

The singer named Muddy Waters listened to the young man. He really liked to hear him sing. He **encouraged** Chuck to make a record. "You're really good!" he said. "Go ahead and try to make the big time." Chuck's first record had a new kind of music. It was called rock and roll. Today many people say that Chuck Berry is the father of rock and roll.

# *How to Use Context*

If you don't know what **encouraged** means, look at the context. Remember, the context is all the other words in the story. Here are some of the other words in the story. They can help you find out what **encouraged** means.

**1.** "You're really good!"

**2.** "Go ahead and try to make the big time."

Find these words in the story about Chuck Berry. Draw a circle around them. What words do you think of when you read the clues? Write a few words on the line below:

_____

Did you write a word like *help*? To *encourage* someone is to *help* someone by what you say or do.

- To use context, read all the words in a story. If some words are too hard, don't stop! Read all the words you can. They may tell you something about the words you could not read.

- When you try to find out what new words mean, remember that some words go together. Think of a meaning that goes with the other words in the story.

**To check your answers, turn to page 62.**

# *Working with Context*

This book is filled with stories. After you read each story, you will answer a question. As you answer the question, you will use the context.

Read the two stories below. In the story about birthday parties, a word is missing. Use the context to choose a word to fit the story. In the story about Aaron Copland, there is a word in **dark letters**. Use the context to figure out what that word means.

◆

### Birthday Parties

Not all birthday parties are _____(1)_____. In one place in the world, everyone has a party on the same day. That day is New Year's Day. In another place, people don't get presents. Instead they give gifts to other people.

_____ **1.** The word that best completes the sentence is

    **A.** sad    **B.** alike   **C.** Monday

◆

### Aaron Copland

Aaron Copland liked music. But he didn't like the songs people were writing. No one could sing them. So Copland began **collecting** the songs that people liked. He listened to many old songs. When he heard a good song, he wrote it down. Then he began writing his own songs. Some had the same tunes as those he had found.

_____ **2.** In this story the word **collecting** means

    **A.** gathering  **B.** jumping  **C.** breaking

**To check your answers, turn to page 62.**

# How to Use This Book

Read the stories in this book. If a word in a story is missing, choose the word that fits. If there is a word in **dark letters** in a story, figure out what that word means.

You can check your answers yourself. Look at pages 59 through 61. You can write the number of answers you got right in the score box at the top of the page.

You can have some fun with context. Read all the stories. Then turn to pages 56 through 58. Work through "Think and Apply." The answers to those questions are on page 62.

### Hints for Better Reading

◆ Keep reading, even if you come to a word you do not know.

◆ The right answer is the word that goes with the other words in the story.

### Challenge Yourself

Try this. Make a list of all the words printed in dark letters. Write a sentence using each one.

# Unit 1

Jumping beans __(1)__ because a worm lives inside. The worm lies still when it is cool. But when it gets warm, the worm moves around. Hold a jumping bean in your hand. The heat from your hand will make the worm move. And that makes the bean jump.

_____ **1.** The word that best completes the sentence is
    **A.** hear      **B.** hop      **C.** push

Look at the stars. They are different colors. The color tells how hot a star is. The hottest stars are blue. White stars are not quite as hot as blue ones. Then come yellow stars, like our sun. They are even __(2)__ than white stars. The coldest stars are the red ones. But even red stars are too hot to visit.

_____ **2.** The word that best completes the sentence is
    **A.** cooler      **B.** brighter      **C.** better

People aren't the only creatures that use tools. Many animals use tools, too. Some monkeys use sticks to catch ants. A monkey pokes a stick into an ant bed. The __(3)__ get angry and bite the stick. Then the monkey pulls the stick out and eats the ants. Ants use tools, too. They make little wagons from leaves. They use the leaves to carry food back to their ant beds.

_____ **3.** The word that best completes the sentence is
    **A.** flies      **B.** insects      **C.** aunts

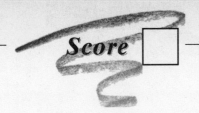

In Ohio there is a place called Great Snake. It is a long, winding dirt wall __(4)__ like a snake. The wall is twenty feet wide and five feet tall. It is also over a thousand feet long. It is so big that you have to be high off the ground to see that it looks like a snake. The snake's mouth looks like it is eating a big egg. The snake's tail winds into a circle.

_____ **4.** The word that best completes the sentence is
   **A.** shaped     **B.** counted     **C.** passed

---

Most puppets are just toys. But a famous painter named Paul Klee made puppets that were art. Klee used strange and unusual things to make his puppets. One puppet had a head made from a pine cone. Another one had a shell nose. Some puppets wore __(5)__ made out of wire and clothes made out of strings.

_____ **5.** The word that best completes the sentence is
   **A.** books     **B.** dogs     **C.** hats

---

Cats and owls can see at night. But no animal can see in complete __(6)__ . People and animals see because of light coming into their eyes. Some animals, like cats and owls, can see in very little light. The light can be so dim that people can't see at all.

_____ **6.** The word that best completes the sentence is
   **A.** day     **B.** forests     **C.** darkness

# Unit 2

Juliette Gordon Low started the Girl Scouts in America. She had heard about the Boy Scouts. She thought it would be a good idea for girls, too. She believed that girls should learn more than just __(1)__ . They should learn how to take care of themselves outdoors. In 1912 there were 18 Girl Scouts. Now there are 3 million Girl Scouts!

_____ **1.** The word that best completes the sentence is
    **A.** saying    **B.** cooking    **C.** walking

---

On New Year's Day in China, there is a __(2)__ . People dress up and march down the street. A special part is the Lion Dance. The lion in the dance is not a real lion. Two people wear a lion suit. One person is the head. The other person is the body. Together they make the lion run, jump, paw the air, and wag its tail.

_____ **2.** The word that best completes the sentence is
    **A.** parade    **B.** neck    **C.** box

---

Cars burn gas in order to go. People burn food instead. You burn about two teaspoons of sugar when you walk a mile. But if you ride a __(3)__ , you can go longer. You can go five miles on two teaspoons of sugar! The wheels do the work instead of your feet.

_____ **3.** The word that best completes the sentence is
    **A.** boat    **B.** bike    **C.** hill

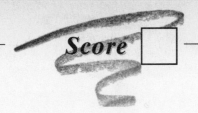

Many good baseball games have been played during the World Series. But one game had the fans on the edge of their seats. It was when the Yankees played the Dodgers. Don Larsen pitched a perfect game for the Yankees. No one on the Dodger team ever hit the ball. No one got a walk, either. Not __(4)__ Dodger got on base! Of course the Yankees won the game.

_____ **4.** The word that best completes the sentence is
      **A.** on        **B.** working     **C.** one

---

Juan Largo has spent seven years learning about black bears. He catches the bears. Then he puts little radios on them. He can track the bears and __(5)__ down what they do. He even knows where they sleep during the winter. Sometimes he puts a tag on a bear's ear. Then he will know that bear when he sees it again.

_____ **5.** The word that best completes the sentence is
      **A.** back       **B.** write       **C.** sing

---

Mangrove trees grow in salt water. Most trees take in water with their roots. Then they let it out through their leaves. When mangroves take in water, they take in salt, too. They let the water and the salt out. After that, mangroves look as if someone __(6)__ salt all over their leaves.

_____ **6.** The word that best completes the sentence is
      **A.** threw      **B.** liked      **C.** grew

# Unit 3

Many travelers like to visit Birdhouse City. They can stay in one of the hotels. Or they might stay in the library or the church! These visitors aren't people. They are birds! And they are guests of the people who live in a small town. The people in the town made almost a hundred birdhouses. Most of the birdhouses look just like __(1)__ in the real town. These houses make up Birdhouse City.

_____ **1.** The word that best completes the sentence is
      **A.** buildings   **B.** friends     **C.** cars

---

Cedo is a monkey. He is the pet of a farm family. He likes to help out on the farm. He helps feed the __(2)__ and load hay into the truck. He even drives the tractor! His owner never makes Cedo work. Cedo works because he thinks it's fun.

_____ **2.** The word that best completes the sentence is
      **A.** berries    **B.** fences     **C.** cows

---

Whales make strange and wonderful __(3)__ that sound like singing. These animals have more than one song. Whales in a group sing the same song for a while. Then they all sing another song. People don't know why whales sing. But they think it may be a kind of talking.

_____ **3.** The word that best completes the sentence is
      **A.** fish      **B.** noises     **C.** smiles

One of the oldest stories in English tells about a fighter. The fighter went to help a king. A mean dragon had been eating the king's people. The brave fighter jumped into the lake where the dragon lived. He killed the dragon, but he was __(4)__. Later he died. People back then thought that it was best to live a short life full of brave acts.

_____ **4.** The word that best completes the sentence is
    **A.** glass      **B.** hurt      **C.** empty

---

Spiders make their webs from thread that comes from their bodies. There are two kinds of thread. One kind is sticky. The other kind is not sticky. Bugs get __(5)__ on the sticky threads. The bugs wiggle the web. The spider feels the wiggles. Then it runs along the threads that are not sticky to get its dinner.

_____ **5.** The word that best completes the sentence is
    **A.** green      **B.** stuck      **C.** friendly

---

The first gas mask was made in 1912. It was called a safety hood. It did not have air tanks. Instead it had a long __(6)__ that hung to the ground. It worked because heat rises. That means that the smoke made by a fire goes up. Near the ground the air is cleaner and cooler. Firefighters breathed only the cooler air.

_____ **6.** The word that best completes the sentence is
    **A.** hose      **B.** flag      **C.** air

When Philip was a boy, settlers came to live near his tribe. Philip's father was chief then. He and the settlers made a peace __(1)__ . Later, Philip became chief. He was called King Philip. He was upset with the settlers. They had built their homes on the tribe's land. King Philip started a war with the settlers. He was killed in the war. The tribe lost its land forever.

_____ **1.** The word that best completes the sentence is
    **A.** sand      **B.** color      **C.** treaty

---

Marbles are made at a factory. Workers first make glass in a large tank. They heat the tank to make the glass hot. Hot glass is thick like syrup. It is poured from a hole at the bottom of the tank. The glass is cut into small chunks. These bits of glass are put on rollers. The rollers change the glass into smooth round balls. They become marbles. The marbles are sorted by size and color. Then they are put into large __(2)__ .

_____ **2.** The word that best completes the sentence is
    **A.** bins      **B.** friends      **C.** stars

---

An underground cave can have a stream in it. A cave fish lives in this stream. The fish is small and white. It can't see because it doesn't have any __(3)__ . It doesn't need them since there is no light in the cave. The cave fish finds food by smell and feel.

_____ **3.** The word that best completes the sentence is
    **A.** arms      **B.** eyes      **C.** teeth

A newt hatches from an egg underwater. This small animal first lives in water. Later in life the newt grows lungs and moves to land. At this stage the newt is bright orange. Other animals can see it easily. But they do not __(4)__ it. They know that the newt's skin will make them sick.

_____ **4.** The word that best completes the sentence is

    **A.** bother    **B.** drive    **C.** iron

---

Scuba divers swim deep in the ocean. They use face masks to see better. They wear fins on their feet to help them swim. To breathe underwater, divers use air tanks. One or two tanks are __(5)__ onto their backs. Then divers can stay underwater for a long time. If the water is cold, they can wear wet suits to stay warm.

_____ **5.** The word that best completes the sentence is

    **A.** imagined    **B.** lost    **C.** strapped

---

A beam of light from the sun looks as if it's white. But it's really made up of many colors. These are the same colors you see in a __(6)__ after a storm. Light that goes from the sun to the earth passes through the air first. Some light bounces off bits of dust in the air. The blue and purple beams in the light are the shortest and bounce the most. They bounce all over the sky. This is why the sky looks blue most of the time.

_____ **6.** The word that best completes the sentence is

    **A.** cup    **B.** rainbow    **C.** face

Death Valley is in California. There is a very old, dry lake bed there. It is called the Racetrack. Marks on the ground show that large rocks there have moved. Some people think that the rocks move because of the weather. When it rains there, the dirt gets muddy. Then strong winds blow the rocks over the __(1)__ ground. The rocks leave marks in the mud. After the mud dries, the marks can still be seen.

_____ **1.** The word that best completes the sentence is
   **A.** beautiful **B.** foolish  **C.** slippery

---

Gerbils are small, furry creatures. They have long back legs and a long, hairy tail. Gerbils are __(2)__ and love to play. They are easy to care for and fun to watch. That is why gerbils make such good pets.

_____ **2.** The word that best completes the sentence is
   **A.** frisky  **B.** lazy   **C.** sleepy

---

People have taken over much of the land. Many wild creatures have lost their homes. Some people worry about this. A few of them formed a group. The group is called the World Wildlife Fund. This group works to save animals and their homes. Many animals live in the rain __(3)__ . The World Wildlife Fund works to keep the trees there from being cut down.

_____ **3.** The word that best completes the sentence is
   **A.** drops  **B.** beds   **C.** forests

At first Sandra was a lawyer. Later she worked as a judge. The president looked at Sandra's work. He saw that she treated people __(4)__ in her court. He asked her to be a judge on the Supreme Court. Sandra Day O'Connor is the first woman ever to hold this job.

_____ **4.** The word that best completes the sentence is
      **A.** poorly     **B.** fairly     **C.** wrongly

A ladybug is a type of small beetle. It has a small, round body. It looks like half of a pea. The ladybug is bright red or yellow. It has black, yellow, red, or white spots on its back. People who grow fruit like this bug. It is helpful. It eats other insects that harm fruit __(5)__ .

_____ **5.** The word that best completes the sentence is
      **A.** crops     **B.** clouds     **C.** games

A river made a __(6)__ in Colorado. It's called Royal Gorge. People used to go through it to get to silver mines. Some people wanted to build a railroad through the deep valley. Two groups of people began to fight. Both of them wanted to build the railroad. Then one group sold out to the other. The railroad was finished.

_____ **6.** The word that best completes the sentence is
      **A.** fan     **B.** canyon     **C.** window

A dust devil is a fast-moving wind. It has dust or sand in it. It starts when hot air rises. The hot air begins to spin. It picks up dust or sand. The spinning __(1)__ of air can stretch more than one thousand feet up into the sky.

_____ **1.** The word that best completes the sentence is
      **A.** street     **B.** column     **C.** feet

---

Hong Kong is an island. On its highest point you can visit Tiger Balm Gardens. These __(2)__ gardens are quite a sight! There is a lovely white tower in the gardens. It is seven stories high. There are also many statues.

_____ **2.** The word that best completes the sentence is
      **A.** wonderful  **B.** terrible     **C.** dirty

---

A peacock is a large bird. The male has very pretty tail feathers. The tail is big. It opens up like a fan. It is full of bright colors. The feathers shine in the light of the sun. A male peacock will show his tail feathers to scare away other males. At other times he will show his tail to make a __(3)__ peacock notice him.

_____ **3.** The word that best completes the sentence is
      **A.** red     **B.** female     **C.** cold

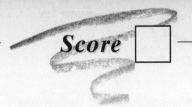
   Donkey races are held in Colorado. The races honor the donkeys that carried packs for miners long ago. In the races people run behind their donkeys. They guide them with ropes. The donkeys wear packs. The packs hold pans, picks, and __(4)__ . These were the miners' tools. The prize for the winner is a thousand dollars.

_____ **4.** The word that best completes the sentence is
     **A.** ovens    **B.** airplanes    **C.** shovels

---

   Some cities have busy streets. Driving a car on these streets can be hard. So some people take the bus. Others like to ride the subway. A subway is like a train. But this __(5)__ travels under the ground. The subway can carry many people. It quickly takes them where they want to go.

_____ **5.** The word that best completes the sentence is
     **A.** town    **B.** sky       **C.** railway

---

   Every __(6)__ you can watch the sun go down. At times the sun looks as if it is being flattened as it sets. But your eyes are being fooled. This happens when the rays of light pass through the earth's air. The air right above the earth is cooler and thicker than the air higher up. This causes the rays of light to bend. The bent light makes the sun look flatter.

_____ **6.** The word that best completes the sentence is
     **A.** evening   **B.** morning   **C.** hour

There was once a big fair in France. The Eiffel Tower was built for it. This tall tower was made out of iron. Today people come from all over to see it. There is a great view from the top. You can even eat in a __(1)__ while you enjoy the view.

_____ **1.** The word that best completes the sentence is
   **A.** restaurant   **B.** book        **C.** garage

---

The Eskimo people live in the far north. Life has changed for them through the years. Most Eskimos once lived by the sea. In the summer they lived in tents. The tents were made of animal skins. In the __(2)__ they moved to new homes. They were made from blocks of dirt or ice. Now most Eskimos live in towns.

_____ **2.** The word that best completes the sentence is
   **A.** water        **B.** afternoon    **C.** winter

---

You might have heard a cat purr when it came up to __(3)__ you. But have you ever wondered how it can make that sound? A cat purrs as it breathes in and out. When the air goes to and from the lungs, it passes through the cat's voice box. The cat can make the space in its voice box smaller. That changes the flow of air. The sound this makes is the cat's purr.

_____ **3.** The word that best completes the sentence is
   **A.** hold         **B.** greet        **C.** feed

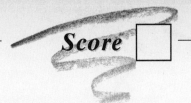

Hail is made of __(4)__ of ice. It can be as small as a pea or as big as a baseball. Hail can break windows and make holes in roofs. It can dent cars and planes. It can also hurt a farmer's crops. Once in a while, it hails so hard that people who are outside can be killed.

_____ **4.** The word that best completes the sentence is
     **A.** branches   **B.** buckets    **C.** lumps

An ice cave is found at the end of a glacier. Light from the sun shines through the ice. This makes the walls of the cave glitter like blue glass. It is very pretty. But an ice cave can have many dangers. As the weather warms, the glacier begins to __(5)__ . Large sheets of ice can fall from the top of the cave. Floods can also happen quickly.

_____ **5.** The word that best completes the sentence is
     **A.** finish    **B.** melt     **C.** sleep

Guppies are small fish. They have tails and fins that look like feathers. Many guppies have bright colors. The colors make them look like shiny __(6)__ . Guppies are pretty fish. Many people like to keep them as pets.

_____ **6.** The word that best completes the sentence is
     **A.** jewels    **B.** letters    **C.** pencils

There are different ways to show what the world looks like. One way is a map. A map is a flat drawing of the world. Another way to show the world is a __(1)__ . This shows that the world is round.

_____ **1.** The word that best completes the sentence is
     **A.** sandwich  **B.** flash      **C.** globe

---

People who work with metal are called welders. They join pieces of metal together. Welders use __(2)__ to make the metal hot. They melt the edges of the pieces and join them together. When the pieces cool, they stay together. Welders always have to think about safety when they work. They wear special clothes so they won't be hurt.

_____ **2.** The word that best completes the sentence is
     **A.** flashlights  **B.** torches     **C.** scissors

---

A parrot is a bird that can talk. It copies the sounds it hears. This bird has special __(3)__ in its neck. The parrot tightens and loosens them. That's how it makes the sounds it hears. A wild parrot sounds like other parrots. But a pet parrot can bark like a dog, ring like a phone, or talk like a person. A pet parrot can even sing and whistle.

_____ **3.** The word that best completes the sentence is
     **A.** candy     **B.** bottles     **C.** muscles

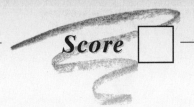
Many plants grow from seeds. Seeds can move from one place to another. They do this in different ways. Some seeds are light. One end may be fuzzy or shaped like wings. The wind carries these seeds away. Other seeds have small hooks. They __(4)__ a ride on an animal's fur or a person's clothes.

_____ **4.** The word that best completes the sentence is

    **A.** hitch     **B.** grow     **C.** spoil

---

A young girl was taken from her home and made a slave. She was brought to the United States and sold. The Wheatley family bought her. Her name was changed to Phillis Wheatley. Her new family taught her how to read and write. Phillis started writing poems. Later she was freed. She once sent a poem to George Washington. He __(5)__ her poem very much. He asked Phillis to visit him.

_____ **5.** The word that best completes the sentence is

    **A.** admired     **B.** wore     **C.** rode

---

A shooting star looks like a streak of light in the sky. It's a piece of metal or stone called a meteor. It passes through the air around the earth. It gets very hot. It gets so hot that it glows. Sometimes there are many in the sky at once. It looks as if it's raining shooting stars. This is called a meteor __(6)__ .

_____ **6.** The word that best completes the sentence is

    **A.** television     **B.** shower     **C.** zoo

Many people like cherry trees. They think that the small pink or white flowers are pretty. They like the sweet smell of the flowers. These people also like the taste of cherries. But not all cherry trees are grown by people. Some grow in the __(1)__ , too.

_____ **1.** The word that best completes the sentence is
      **A.** dark      **B.** wild      **C.** freezer

A fish farm is a place for growing fish. Fish eggs are placed in large tanks. The tanks are filled with __(2)__ . Over time the eggs grow and hatch. Workers feed the fish every day. The fish get bigger. The fish are sold when they are big enough to eat. Someday all of the fish we eat might come from fish farms.

_____ **2.** The word that best completes the sentence is
      **A.** water      **B.** juice      **C.** money

Roanoke Island is in the United States. It is off the East Coast. Settlers once came from England to live there. Life on the island was hard. Most of the settlers went back to England. Then new settlers came to the island. Their leader was John White. He sailed back to England for supplies. But England was at war. John could not get back to the island for three years. By then he could not find the settlers. They had all __(3)__ .

_____ **3.** The word that best completes the sentence is
      **A.** fainted      **B.** worked      **C.** disappeared

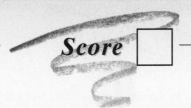
There's a museum in Ohio. It's called the Cleveland Health Education Museum. People go there to learn how the human body works. There are huge models of an eye, an ear, and a tooth. The models are big enough for people to walk inside. People come from all over the __(4)__ to see this museum.

_____ **4.** The word that best completes the sentence is
    **A.** turtle     **B.** engine     **C.** world

---

The scorpion can be found in warm __(5)__ . It's a small animal. It has four pairs of legs. The scorpion has two large claws in front. It grabs and crushes its live food with these claws. The scorpion has from six to twelve eyes. But it is best known for its tail. The scorpion stings with its tail. The sting is very painful, but it is usually not deadly.

_____ **5.** The word that best completes the sentence is
    **A.** shirts     **B.** countries     **C.** moons

---

Light can pass through some objects, such as glass. You can see through these objects. But light can't pass through other objects. You cannot see through these. On the side away from the source of light, there is a dark place on the ground. This shows where the light has been blocked. The dark spot is called a __(6)__ .

_____ **6.** The word that best completes the sentence is
    **A.** painting     **B.** baby     **C.** shadow

A beaver's house is called a lodge. The lodge is built on a pond or a river. It is made with branches and twigs. The beaver enters the lodge from a tunnel under the water. Inside the lodge is a room. The __(1)__ of the room is above the water. The beaver can dry off and stay warm in the room of its lodge.

_____ **1.** The word that best completes the sentence is
  **A.** floor          **B.** knee          **C.** shoe

---

Charles Drew was good in sports. He wanted to teach others how to play sports. So he became a __(2)__ . Later, Charles went back to school. He wanted to be a doctor. While in school Charles studied about blood. He found a way to store blood. Then it could be used when it was needed. Many people's lives were saved. Charles won many awards for his work.

_____ **2.** The word that best completes the sentence is
  **A.** pilot          **B.** dancer          **C.** coach

---

Mount St. Helens is a volcano. It is in the state of Washington. It was quiet for almost fifty years. Then one day Mount St. Helens exploded. Ash was thrown into the air. Lava flowed, and hot rocks flew out. Melting snow caused floods. Forests caught on fire. The __(3)__ where people stayed were burned. Some people lost their lives.

_____ **3.** The word that best completes the sentence is
  **A.** cabins          **B.** meals          **C.** nights

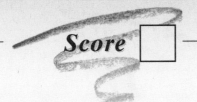
A mud skipper is a fish. Its body looks like that of a fish, but it has a head like a frog. The mud skipper's eyes stick out from its head. It moves its eyes around to look for food. If the mud skipper can't find food in the water, it __(4)__ out onto the land. There it stands on its back fins. It hops around as it hunts for food.

_____ **4.** The word that best completes the sentence is
    **A.** winks    **B.** crawls    **C.** studies

The oilbird lives in South America. It looks like an owl. It hunts for food at night. During the day it flies into a dark cave where it lives. The oilbird can find its way in the dark. It will screech or make a clicking sound. Then it listens for the sound to bounce back as an __(5)__ . This tells the bird where to fly.

_____ **5.** The word that best completes the sentence is
    **A.** echo    **B.** elephant    **C.** elf

Pine cones grow on pine trees. In the spring some of the cones make pollen. The pollen looks like grains of yellow powder. The __(6)__ carries the pollen to new places. Some pollen lands on pine cones that don't make pollen. These pine cones use the pollen to make seeds. When the seeds are ripe, they fall to the ground. They may take root and grow up to be new pine trees.

_____ **6.** The word that best completes the sentence is
    **A.** bicycle    **B.** wind    **C.** feather

The day lily is a plant. It has __(1)__ without leaves. At the end of each one is a group of flowers. These flowers are yellow or orange. During the summer two or three of them bloom each day. They bloom when the sun comes up. Then they die when the sun sets.

_____ **1.** The word that best completes the sentence is
    **A.** fences    **B.** apartments  **C.** stalks

---

There's a museum where you can learn about the desert. You can see plants and animals that live in the desert. Snakes, bobcats, and elf owls are just a few of these animals. There are many kinds of __(2)__ plants. This museum is in an Arizona desert. It is called the Arizona-Sonora Desert Museum.

_____ **2.** The word that best completes the sentence is
    **A.** jolly    **B.** breakfast    **C.** cactus

---

A barnyard pig takes a bath in mud. This is not because it likes to be dirty. In fact it would like cool, clean water much better. But a pig must find a way to cool off. It can't __(3)__ to stay cool the way people do. So it will lie in the mud to stay cool. The thick mud also helps the pig's skin. Insects can't bite it, and the sun won't burn it.

_____ **3.** The word that best completes the sentence is
    **A.** fly    **B.** sweat    **C.** kick

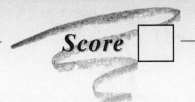
A rodeo is great fun. It reminds us of what life was like for cowboys in the Old West. Men and women try to win prizes at a rodeo. They can choose to be in many kinds of __(4)__ . Some people like to ride a wild horse or a bull. Others like to rope a calf or throw a steer onto its back.

_____ **4.** The word that best completes the sentence is
       **A.** grass      **B.** islands      **C.** contests

The wart hog is a type of pig that lives in Africa. The wart hog is a light gray color. It has short, stiff hairs on its body. It also has a __(5)__ of longer hair that runs down its neck. The hog has a large head that is flat in front. It has long, curved teeth, or tusks. The hog gets its name from the three pairs of bumps on its head, called warts.

_____ **5.** The word that best completes the sentence is
       **A.** basket      **B.** mane      **C.** party

Long ago, people rushed west to hunt for gold. They lived in __(6)__ near gold mines. Then they built homes. Soon whole towns grew up near the mines. But many of these towns didn't last long. When people had found all of the gold, they went to a new place. The towns they left behind became ghost towns. Only the empty buildings and streets were left.

_____ **6.** The word that best completes the sentence is
       **A.** camps      **B.** chairs      **C.** dollars

A cat's tongue feels rough. This is true for all cats. House cats, lions, and tigers all have rough tongues. A cat uses its tongue in many ways. It __(1)__ itself to brush its fur. The cat removes dirt and loose hair this way. The cat also uses its rough tongue to scrape meat from a bone. When the cat is through, the bone is clean.

_____ **1.** The word that best completes the sentence is
      **A.** paints    **B.** licks    **C.** frightens

---

Trees are important. People make many things from trees. Trees are also helpful. They hold the dirt in place and help make the air we breathe. Trees are also the home for many creatures. So we need to be sure we __(2)__ the trees. When old trees are cut down, new ones must be planted.

_____ **2.** The word that best completes the sentence is
      **A.** forget    **B.** find    **C.** save

---

Young people can join the Four-H Club. The goal of this club is to improve head, heart, hands, and health. Members have a chance to learn skills. They also find out about careers. Members try out jobs by working on __(3)__. These jobs might deal with plants, animals, food, or safety.

_____ **3.** The word that best completes the sentence is
      **A.** ice    **B.** moments    **C.** projects

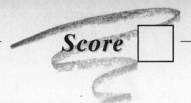

Germs are living things. But they are very small. They are so small that you need a microscope to see them. Germs can be found in all places. Many germs are harmless. But others can make you sick if they get inside your __(4)__ . There are ways you can keep safe from these germs. Be sure to wash your hands, keep cuts clean, and stay away from someone who has a cold.

_____ **4.** The word that best completes the sentence is

    **A.** body      **B.** glasses      **C.** homework

---

*Alvin* is the name of a small ship. People use *Alvin* to study the sea. The ship goes under the water. The people ride inside of it. The deep sea is very dark, so *Alvin* has big headlights. They light up parts of the sea. Then __(5)__ take pictures. A long hook scoops up samples from the sea floor. Later, people study these pictures and samples.

_____ **5.** The word that best completes the sentence is

    **A.** cats      **B.** cameras      **C.** nails

---

The mimosa is a plant. It has parts that look like feathers. These parts are made from two rows of tiny leaves. When it rains, the leaves lie open. If an animal touches any of the leaves, they __(6)__ up. But the leaves open again the next time it rains.

_____ **6.** The word that best completes the sentence is

    **A.** sit      **B.** fold      **C.** dress

Some snakes have four eyes. They have eyes that see in the day. But they also have two more eyes. These eyes can see heat. Snakes use these eyes to look for food. A snake **gazes** all around with its special eyes. Its eyes cannot see a plant. Plants do not give off any heat. But the eyes can see a mouse. A mouse is warm and good for snakes to eat.

_____ **1.** In this story the word **gazes** means

     **A.** stares    **B.** gives    **C.** adds

---

Deep inside, the earth is made of very hot rock. The rock is so hot that it can turn water into steam. In some places this steam comes out of cracks in the ground. In other places people pipe the steam up from deep in the ground. People use this steam **energy** to warm their homes.

_____ **2.** In this story the word **energy** means

     **A.** ice    **B.** power    **C.** stream

---

What is vegetable art? Ask Bob Spohn. For fifty years Spohn has **whittled** faces and animals out of large vegetables. He uses a knife to make the faces. Then he paints them. He once made a smiling face from a giant pumpkin. The pumpkin was almost a yard high and weighed 110 pounds!

_____ **3.** In this story the word **whittled** means

     **A.** drawn    **B.** shaken    **C.** cut

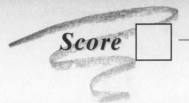
Some people once used pictures instead of letters for writing. One picture was called the tooth. It was **curved** like a big chewing tooth. The shape had two bends in it. Later, people drew the tooth on its side. It looked like a snake. Today we call this letter *S*.

_____ **4.** In this story the word **curved** means
     **A.** stopped    **B.** asleep    **C.** rounded

How is a new coin made? People first make a model. This shows how they want the coin to look. The **model** is many times larger than a real coin. Then a worker makes a small copy of the model. The copy is the master coin. Copies of the master coin are used to stamp the design onto new coins.

_____ **5.** In this story the word **model** means
     **A.** size    **B.** pattern    **C.** hope

Most animals need **protection** from heat and cold. Some have hair that keeps them warm in the winter. Animals that live in hot places have different hair. Their hair keeps them cool in summer. Animals that spend much of their time in cold water have a lot of fat. This fat helps keep them from getting too cold.

_____ **6.** In this story the word **protection** means
     **A.** safety    **B.** water    **C.** lunch

Bluebirds are pretty birds. Their head and wings are bright blue. Most bluebirds have some red on their chest. The bluebird's song is sweet. People are worried about this small bird. There used to be many of them in towns and forests. Now bluebirds are becoming very **rare**.

_____ **1.** In this story the word **rare** means
　　　　**A.** hard to find **B.** mean 　　**C.** fun to catch

---

Most people think sea birds live only near the sea. But **numerous** sea birds fly toward land, too. In the spring and summer, they go to rivers and lakes to nest. They go to the same place every year.

_____ **2.** In this story the word **numerous** means
　　　　**A.** troubled 　**B.** sick 　　　**C.** many

---

Itzhak Perlman is a great violin player. As a boy he heard beautiful music on the radio. When he was just three years old, he **requested** a violin. He wanted to play beautiful music, too. At first his parents bought him a toy violin. But he knew it did not sound right. So they bought him a real one. Now he plays the violin all over the world.

_____ **3.** In this story the word **requested** means
　　　　**A.** took away **B.** asked for 　**C.** got back

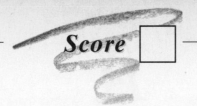

You spill a drink on your clothes. What do you do? First find some club soda. Rub it on your clothes where the **stain** is. Dry your clothes with a towel. The spot should be gone.

_____ **4.** In this story the word **stain** means
       **A.** mark      **B.** button      **C.** machine

The Air and Space Museum has **historic** airplanes. These planes were fixed up by museum workers. The workers took the planes apart. They made new parts for the ones that were worn out. Then they put the planes back together just like new. This job took a long time. Two people worked about two years to fix up each old plane.

_____ **5.** In this story the word **historic** means
       **A.** high      **B.** sweet      **C.** old

There is a bird that can swim underwater and climb trees. It has claws on its wings. These birds build their nests over rivers and lakes. Sometimes the baby birds are afraid of other animals. Then they dive into the water and swim to another tree. They use their wing claws to climb up to a high branch. These birds use many tricks to **outwit** their enemies.

_____ **6.** In this story the word **outwit** means
       **A.** corner      **B.** attack      **C.** fool

A volcano blew up in Italy long ago. Some towns were covered by rivers of melted rock. One town was covered by 66 feet of hot black rock. It happened in just a few minutes. The towns were hidden under the rock for hundreds of years. When people found them again, they looked just as they had looked long ago. The towns were **preserved** by the rock.

_____ **1.** In this story the word **preserved** means
    **A.** tricked    **B.** kept the same **C.** moved

---

Some paintings are pictures of fruit or people. But some paintings are pictures of colors and shapes. These paintings **represent** ideas instead of things. A yellow line could remind us of anger. A red circle could remind us of love.

_____ **2.** In this story the word **represent** means
    **A.** cover up    **B.** stand for    **C.** step on

---

Round, metal balls are used in guns. These balls are called shot. They are made in a shot tower. The shot tower is very tall. Metal is melted at the top. Then it is poured through tiny holes. The drops of metal **plunge** to the ground. On the way down, they form round balls. These balls land in cool water at the bottom of the tower.

_____ **3.** In this story the word **plunge** means
    **A.** fall    **B.** break    **C.** climb

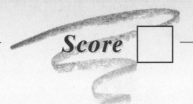
One bird really can swim like a fish. It is called the loon. This bird has been found more than one hundred feet below the water's **surface**. The bird can also fly. But it cannot walk. Its legs are very far back on its body. When it tries to stand up, it falls over.

_____ **4.** In this story the word **surface** means

     **A.** hole      **B.** top      **C.** ribbon

How do desert animals get water? Some catch it on their bodies. Some snakes, lizards, and bugs sleep out in the open air. Cool winds blow during the night. These winds take water from the desert air. By morning small drops of this water have landed on the bodies of the animals. They drink the water by licking it. The wind and the water are **necessary** for desert animals. Without the wind they might die.

_____ **5.** In this story the word **necessary** means

     **A.** thanked    **B.** pitched    **C.** needed

Doctors did a study on how some people stay thin. They found that nervous people use more energy. They walk the floor. They tap their toes. They drum their fingers. In one day these people burn up the energy it takes to run five miles. This finding may lead to a new kind of exercise. People will **squirm** the pounds away!

_____ **6.** In this story the word **squirm** means

     **A.** wiggle    **B.** jump    **C.** run

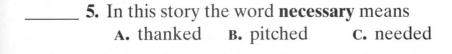

You may not know Clara Barton's name. You know her work, though. She started the American Red Cross. During the Civil War, Barton went to battles to help wounded soldiers. After the war she saw that many soldiers could nct find their families. She started to **trace** the missing people. Later she learned about the Red Cross in Europe. She decided that the United States needed a Red Cross, too.

_____ **1.** In this story the word **trace** means

      **A.** mail       **B.** teach       **C.** find

---

In the ocean, waves look like moving mountains. But when they get close to a beach, they begin to fall over. Why does this happen? Close to the shore the water is **shallow**. The waves that come from the deep sea are very tall. Then they get close to shore. They try to stand tall, but they fall over.

_____ **2.** In this story the word **shallow** means

      **A.** not slow       **B.** not deep       **C.** not salty

---

Benny Goodman was a band leader. He was called the King of Swing. His band played music that had a new sound. This swing music was **snappy**. It had a strong beat. People danced a fast new dance to this music. It was also called the swing.

_____ **3.** In this story the word **snappy** means

      **A.** tall       **B.** gray       **C.** quick

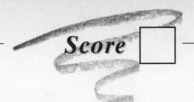

People have loved amber for thousands of years. Amber looks like stone. But it really comes from the gum of trees. This gum fell to the ground long ago. It was covered with dirt and then became hard. There it stayed until it was found. Pieces of amber can be **polished** to make beads and rings. To do this you must rub the amber for a very long time.

_____ **4.** In this story the word **polished** means
      **A.** shined     **B.** missed     **C.** hidden

---

Not all sharks are mean. Nurse sharks look bad, but they almost never hurt people. Instead they stay on the bottom of the ocean. They swim along, **sucking** in sand, crabs, snails, and tiny fish. They spit out the sand and eat the animals!

_____ **5.** In this story the word **sucking** means
      **A.** rolling     **B.** pulling     **C.** calling

---

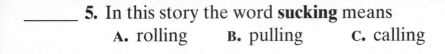

Some farmers in China were digging a well. They dug deeper and deeper. Suddenly a shovel struck something hard. A farmer bent down and pushed the dirt away. He found himself looking into a person's eyes. The person was made of clay. Scientists later dug up the area. Under the earth were three thousand clay **warriors**. Some were on horses. Many carried spears and knives. All of them were as big as real people.

_____ **6.** In this story the word **warriors** means
      **A.** fighters     **B.** pots     **C.** animals

The Sears Tower is a tall building in Chicago. It took three years to **plan** the design. Then it took four more years to build. The Sears Tower has 110 floors. It has more than 100 elevators. In just seconds you can ride up to the Skydeck. You can look down at the city from the deck. It is a great view.

_____ **1.** In this story the word **plan** means
      **A.** prepare    **B.** eat        **C.** understand

Gravity is the force that pulls you toward the earth. The pull is strongest when you're on the earth's surface. That's because the pull from the whole earth is **below** you. You could change this by going into a deep mine. Then some of the earth would be above you. You would be pulled up and down. If you could go to the center of the earth, you would be pulled the same amount in all directions. You would float!

_____ **2.** In this story the word **below** means
      **A.** together    **B.** under      **C.** above

Jane Addams cared about people. She wanted to help the poor. Jane gave **lectures** to crowds of people. She told them about changes that had to be made. Jane helped change unfair laws. She set up many programs to help the poor. She started day-care centers and classes.

_____ **3.** In this story the word **lectures** means
      **A.** speeches    **B.** groups      **C.** holidays

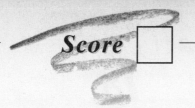
The pine marten is a type of weasel. It is about two feet long and has brown fur. The pine marten lives in pine and spruce forests. It spends most of its life in the tops of the trees. This weasel will **follow** and catch a red squirrel or bird to eat. Once in a while, it will come down to the ground to look for food. It likes to eat small animals, fish, nuts, and fruits.

_____ **4.** In this story the word **follow** means
      **A.** lead       **B.** promise      **C.** chase

Neon is a type of gas found in the air. It is used in some **lamps** for homes and businesses. It is used to fill tubes for store signs, too. Now artists have found a new way to use neon. They make pictures with the neon-filled tubes. When the pictures are done, they are plugged in. People are amazed by the bright colors in neon art.

_____ **5.** In this story the word **lamps** means
      **A.** barns       **B.** coats       **C.** lights

Bobwhites are birds that live in groups. They search for insects and seeds in the woods. If the bobwhites come to a **clearing**, they run across it. They want to get back to the safety of the woods as fast as they can. At night these birds form a circle before they go to sleep. This helps them stay warm. They can also fly off in all directions if there's any danger.

_____ **6.** In this story the word **clearing** means
      **A.** river       **B.** field       **C.** mountain

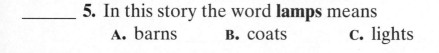

Spanish explorers came to America long ago. They brought horses with them. Some of these horses got **loose** and ran away. Over the years the number of wild horses grew. They became known as mustangs. Today there are still some herds of wild mustangs. They live in the West.

_____ **1.** In this story the word **loose** means

      **A.** caught    **B.** free     **C.** hurt

---

The South Pole is the coldest place on the earth. It's in the middle of Antarctica. The snow at the South Pole is more than a mile deep. But very little snow falls there. It snows far less than an inch each year. The little bit of snow that does fall can't melt. It lies on top of a solid layer of ice. For over a million years, the snow has **pressed** together to form this ice.

_____ **2.** In this story the word **pressed** means

      **A.** pushed    **B.** hopped    **C.** emptied

---

The people of Greece have told tales about the Cyclops for a long time. The Cyclops was said to be a huge monster. His body looked like a human's. But the Cyclops had just one eye. It was in the middle of his forehead. The Cyclops lived on an island. He made his home in a cave there. He liked to eat people who came to his island. So the people feared this **savage** beast.

_____ **3.** In this story the word **savage** means

      **A.** kind      **B.** wet      **C.** cruel

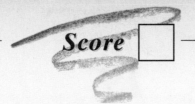
The first jigsaw puzzle was made in England. It was made by a teacher. The teacher wanted his students to learn about the map of England. He **glued** a map to a sheet of wood. Then he cut the map along county lines. The students loved working the puzzle. They learned all about the map of England.

_____ **4.** In this story the word **glued** means

      **A.** served    **B.** dressed    **C.** pasted

---

Squanto was a Native American. He was taken to Spain as a slave. But he ran away to England. Then Squanto sailed back to his home. He met the Pilgrims living at Plymouth. They were **nearly** dead. They had no food. Squanto helped the Pilgrims. He taught them how to plant corn. He showed them where to fish and hunt.

_____ **5.** In this story the word **nearly** means

      **A.** tomorrow  **B.** almost    **C.** soon

---

Most wild animals have color in their fur or skin. But some do not. These animals are called albinos. They are white or very **pale**. Their white color makes them easy to see. Albinos can't sneak up on smaller animals. They also can't hide. So they die or become food for others.

_____ **6.** In this story the word **pale** means

      **A.** light    **B.** dark    **C.** happy

You may not see many wild animals during the day. But there is a way to tell where wild animals have been. You can look for their tracks. Tracks are the prints their feet leave on the ground. You can **determine** which wild creatures left the tracks. The size and shape of the tracks will give you clues.

_____ **1.** In this story the word **determine** means
    **A.** speak     **B.** repair     **C.** tell

---

Waves often wash pretty shells up on the beach. But shells are not the only **appealing** things the waves bring. Sea beans are also washed up on shore. They are seeds and fruits from distant lands. They can be found on the beach from late March through the first part of summer.

_____ **2.** In this story the word **appealing** means
    **A.** brave     **B.** interesting    **C.** ugly

---

Maya Lin drew a design for a contest. Her design won and was built. Thousands of names were carved on two walls of shiny, black stone. The names were Americans who had died in the Vietnam War. At first people thought that the stone was ugly. They **disliked** it. But then they began to change their minds. They found that they could walk up to the walls. They could touch the names of loved ones.

_____ **3.** In this story the word **disliked** means
    **A.** lost     **B.** tricked     **C.** hated

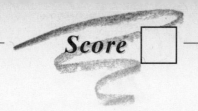

The sap from a poison ivy plant causes itchy bumps on your skin. It is best to know what this plant looks like. Poison ivy grows as a vine or a shrub. The leaves are always in groups of three on each stem. But the color, size, and shape of the leaves can be different for each plant. Poison ivy **blooms** in the first part of summer. It has small blossoms that turn into berries.

_____ **4.** In this story the word **blooms** means

        **A.** flowers    **B.** cries    **C.** travels

---

The Great Dane is a type of dog. It has a thick coat of short hair. Its hair can be black, tan, or white. The Great Dane is very large and strong. For this reason it can be used as a **guard** dog. But a Great Dane is also very gentle. So it makes a good pet, too.

_____ **5.** In this story the word **guard** means

        **A.** funny    **B.** lazy    **C.** watch

---

People wrote with secret codes long ago. Today many people still use secret codes. Two types of codes are used the most. In one kind of code, symbols take the place of letters. These symbols can be letters, numbers, or words. A code book is used to read the message. The other kind of code changes the **arrangement** of the letters. The letters have to be unscrambled to read the message.

_____ **6.** In this story the word **arrangement** means

        **A.** order    **B.** shape    **C.** face

Susan Williams likes to go to bubble-gum-blowing contests. She blows bubbles as big as bike wheels. She blows bubbles inside of bubbles. She can even blow them under the water. Susan has won prizes and broken records. She is a world **champion**.

_____ **1.** In this story the word **champion** means

    **A.** family     **B.** winner     **C.** summer

---

The frostweed is a plant that grows in Texas. It grows best in the shade or in moist dirt. It is found under large trees and on the banks of creeks. This plant has a tall stem with a group of white flowers on the end. When the first freeze of the year comes, the plant's stem **splits**. Then sap leaks out. The sap freezes around the stem. It looks like ribbons or clusters of flowers.

_____ **2.** In this story the word **splits** means

    **A.** shuts     **B.** cracks     **C.** wanders

---

The first newspaper was a letter. It told the news. The letter was sent by messenger. It went to people who lived in far-off lands. Hundreds of years later, a news sheet was used. It was written by hand each day. Then it was **hung** up for all to read. Much later the Chinese carved wooden blocks. They printed a paper. Now the newspaper is a quick way to get the news.

_____ **3.** In this story the word **hung** means

    **A.** put     **B.** sawed     **C.** grown

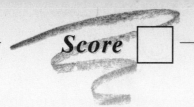
There was once a French **physician** who took care of sick people. In his spare time, he looked through a telescope. One day he was looking at the sun. He saw a round, black spot move in front of it. He thought that the spot was a planet that no one knew about. He told others about the planet. They named this new planet Vulcan. Today people know that the spot was not a planet at all. They think it might have been a sunspot.

_____ **4.** In this story the word **physician** means
      **A.** doctor     **B.** plant     **C.** teacher

Some animals have eyes that glow in the dark. This happens when light goes into their eyes. The light hits an area in the back of the eye. Then it bounces back through the eye. These animals can use the light as it goes in and as it comes out. They use the **extra** light to see at night.

_____ **5.** In this story the word **extra** means
      **A.** cold     **B.** thin     **C.** added

The flashlight fish has lights that turn on and off. The lights are the glow of a special place under each eye. This fish uses its lights in many ways. It can use them to find food. It sends **signals** with them to other flashlight fish. The fish can cover its lights with a lid. This way an enemy can't find it.

_____ **6.** In this story the word **signals** means
      **A.** plates     **B.** wheels     **C.** messages

The Big Dipper can be seen in the northern sky at night. It has seven stars. They form the **outline** of a pot. Three of the stars make the dipper's handle. Four of the stars make the rest of the pot. Two stars in the Big Dipper are brighter than the rest. They are called pointer stars. They can be used to find the North Star.

_____ **1.** In this story the word **outline** means

      **A.** shape      **B.** river      **C.** candle

---

The *Mary Celeste* was a ship. It set sail more than one hundred years ago. On board were the captain and a **crew** of eight sailors. One month after the *Mary Celeste* left, it was seen by another ship's captain. He saw that the *Mary Celeste* was going the wrong way. The captain went to find out what was wrong. He saw that no one was on board. He never found out what had happened to the people on the *Mary Celeste.*

_____ **2.** In this story the word **crew** means

      **A.** ladder      **B.** rock      **C.** team

---

A stinkbug is an insect. It can be green or brown. But it can also be other colors. A stinkbug has a special trick. It uses its back legs or its stomach to make a bad smell. When the stinkbug gets scared, it can **spray** out the smelly stuff.

_____ **3.** In this story the word **spray** means

      **A.** splash      **B.** climb      **C.** find

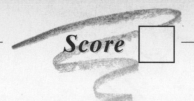
Puppets have been used for thousands of years. They are a good way to tell a story. There are many kinds of puppets. Some are worked from above by strings or wires. Others are worked from below by rods or hands. Puppets can be any shape or size. Some are **miniature**, while others are almost life-size.

_____ **4.** In this story the word **miniature** means
         **A.** early       **B.** little       **C.** magic

---

Wood ducks live in woods near lakes or swamps. They nest in tree **holes**. Once there were many wood ducks. Then people moved into the woods and cut down the trees where the ducks lived. They also hunted the ducks for food. People saw that soon there would not be any wood ducks left. They have worked hard to save these ducks.

_____ **5.** In this story the word **holes** means
         **A.** openings    **B.** bridges     **C.** schools

---

Long ago, people would just sing when they danced. At some point they started adding other sounds. People would snap their fingers, clap their hands, or stamp their feet. Then they learned to **beat** on drums. Whistles were made from clay, bone, and wood. Music made from strings came sometime later.

_____ **6.** In this story the word **beat** means
         **A.** write       **B.** blow       **C.** hit

# Unit 22

Long ago, people used candles for light. They made the candles by hand. Fat from sheep, oxen, bear, or deer was used for the waxy part. The fat was melted in a large **kettle**. About six strings were hung from a rod. These strings became the wicks. The strings were slowly dipped into the wax. The hot wax stuck to the strings. The candles were dipped until they were thick.

_____ **1.** In this story the word **kettle** means

     **A.** home     **B.** arm     **C.** pot

The butcher's broom is a plant. People sometimes dry the branches from this plant to make brooms. When the butcher's broom is alive, it's a dark green **shrub**. It does not have leaves. But its small branches are flat and look like leaves. Tiny flowers bloom in the middle of the small branches. The flowers change into red berries.

_____ **2.** In this story the word **shrub** means

     **A.** cow     **B.** bush     **C.** apron

A blenny is a fish. It can be very **sly**. The blenny can hide at the bottom of the sea. This fish is hard to see because it can change color. The blenny can also jump out of the water. It will sit on rocks near the water. It finds food in the rocks.

_____ **3.** In this story the word **sly** means

     **A.** tricky     **B.** hollow     **C.** proud

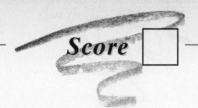
Roller-coaster cars are hooked to a chain at first. A motor on the ground runs the chain. It pulls the cars to the top of the first hill. Then the cars are unhooked. When the cars roll down hill, they speed up. The cars slow down as they **coast** up the next hill. They speed up again as they go down it. Each hill is a bit lower than the last. The cars can't go up a hill that is as high as the one they just came down.

_____ **4.** In this story the word **coast** means
      **A.** move     **B.** park     **C.** leak

---

Stevie Wonder was born blind. This did not stop him from using his talent. He found that he was good with music. He learned how to play many instruments. He wrote his own songs. At the age of twelve, he sang his first hit. Since then he has made many **albums**. He has even written music for a movie.

_____ **5.** In this story the word **albums** means
      **A.** oranges     **B.** buttons     **C.** records

---

Some people tell stories about Bunyips. Bunyips are said to live in lakes and rivers. There are many kinds of these strange beasts. Some are part person and part fish. Others look like big, brown creatures. They are **shaggy** and have big mouths. Still others look like dogs with webbed feet.

_____ **6.** In this story the word **shaggy** means
      **A.** hairy     **B.** silly     **C.** empty

A prism is a bar made out of glass. It has flat sides. It shows the colors in a light beam. The light is bent as it goes in one side of the prism. Then it is bent again on its way out the other side. Red, orange, yellow, green, blue, and **violet** light waves are in the beam. They are different lengths. So they bend different amounts. This makes the colors spread out as they go through the prism.

_____ **1.** In this story the word **violet** means
      **A.** purple     **B.** easy     **C.** rich

---

The King's Camel Race is run in Saudi Arabia. The race is about twelve miles long. Any camel owner may ride in the race. The riders talk to their camels. They **coax** their camels to go faster. They know the rider who comes in first will win many prizes.

_____ **2.** In this story the word **coax** means
      **A.** visit     **B.** urge     **C.** paste

---

The mouse lemur is a small animal. It spends most of its life in the tops of trees. It leaps around to look for food. The mouse lemur has strong fingers and toes. It grabs tree limbs. It uses its thick tail to stay **stable**. This way it does not fall.

_____ **3.** In this story the word **stable** means
      **A.** loose     **B.** sweet     **C.** balanced

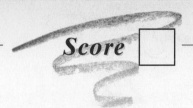

The first zipper was made about one hundred years ago. It did not work well. At times it would **jam**. Other times it would just pop open. So it was not used much. About twenty years later, a better zipper was made. But most people still didn't use it. It took almost twenty more years before the zipper was widely used.

_____ **4.** In this story the word **jam** means
      **A.** joke      **B.** laugh      **C.** stick

---

Native Americans wrote with pictures. They drew pictures on many things. They used hides, wooden poles, and tree bark. The paint was made from flowers, plants, grass, dirt, and rocks. A brush for the paint was made from a piece of buffalo bone. Some pictures told stories. Others were used to **record** things that happened.

_____ **5.** In this story the word **record** means
      **A.** note      **B.** hunt      **C.** pack

---

Rivers show signs that tell how old they are. Young rivers are very narrow. The water flows quickly. Most young rivers have waterfalls. Older rivers are wider. The oldest rivers bend back and forth through a **broad** valley. They move slowly and sometimes flood the valley.

_____ **6.** In this story the word **broad** means
      **A.** young      **B.** wide      **C.** strange

The spadefoot toad lives in the desert. It has a hard edge on the inside of its back feet. It uses its back feet to dig a hole in the dirt. The toad stays in the hole during the heat of the day. It comes out at night to eat. It also comes out on warm, rainy days. It lays its eggs in a **puddle** of water from the rain. The eggs hatch and grow before the water dries up.

_____ **1.** In this story the word **puddle** means

     **A.** balloon    **B.** pool       **C.** lock

---

There's a special college in the United States. It's for students who have **difficulty** hearing. Some of them have never heard words before. So it is hard for them to learn how to speak. These students can still talk with others. They use their hands to talk. They make signs with their hands. The signs stand for one letter, one word, or a group of words.

_____ **2.** In this story the word **difficulty** means

     **A.** problems  **B.** pennies    **C.** places

---

There's an animal called the mongoose. It's about two feet long. It's covered with soft, brown **fur**. The mongoose sleeps in a hole at night. During the day it looks for food. Snakes are one of the things it likes to eat. The mongoose is well known for killing deadly snakes.

_____ **3.** In this story the word **fur** means

     **A.** world     **B.** grain      **C.** hair

The Chicago River is in Illinois. It goes through the city of Chicago. People used to dump their **trash** into the river. This dirty water flowed to a nearby lake. Soon the lake water was dirty. Then the people found a way to keep the lake clean. They built dams on the river. The dams forced the water to flow away from the lake. Now the lake water stays clean.

_____ **4.** In this story the word **trash** means

      **A.** banana     **B.** garbage     **C.** sign

---

There's a special place in Michigan. It's a museum for children. The children come to learn about science. Some come from school. The museum sends a special truck for them. The children look at science **kits** during the ride. They look at rocks, models, and books.

_____ **5.** In this story the word **kits** means

      **A.** packages    **B.** organs     **C.** hills

---

Forest rangers watch for a fire in the woods. They try to stop a fire before it spreads. But this is not an easy job. Most fires start where the woods are thick. There aren't any roads in the middle of the woods. So firefighters can't drive to the fire. They must **parachute** from a plane to get there.

_____ **6.** In this story the word **parachute** means

      **A.** shoot     **B.** refuse     **C.** jump

The desert is a dry place, but there are sudden rainstorms at times. The rains are **brief** but heavy. There's too much rain for it all to sink into the ground. A river forms in the low spots of the desert. The river is called a wadi. It flows fast and destroys many things.

_____ **1.** In this story the word **brief** means
    **A.** fair      **B.** fun      **C.** short

James Wide worked for the railroad. He was in a wheelchair. So he had a pet baboon that helped him. The baboon would push James to and from work. James taught his baboon how to open and **shut** the track switches. Soon the baboon knew when the trains were coming. It would switch the tracks right on time.

_____ **2.** In this story the word **shut** means
    **A.** play      **B.** begin      **C.** close

Three hundred years ago there were many dodoes. These large birds lived on a small island. But sailors started coming to the island. They killed many dodoes for food. The sailors brought **hogs** and dogs with them. These animals broke the dodoes' eggs. Soon there weren't any more dodoes left.

_____ **3.** In this story the word **hogs** means
    **A.** pigs      **B.** boats      **C.** days

The tree frog lives in trees. It leaps from branch to branch. The frog does this by using the sticky pads on the ends of its long toes. A tree frog is hard to see. It can change its color. The tree frog can be green like a leaf or brown like tree bark. You might hear a tree frog, even though you don't see it. The frog makes a **peeping** sound.

_____ **4.** In this story the word **peeping** means

        **A.** squeaking  **B.** working    **C.** coloring

---

There's an island called Yap in the Pacific Ocean. The people there don't buy or sell things. They only trade one thing for another. They write down the trades on huge coins. These coins are made of stone and can be twelve feet high. There's a hole through the middle of the coins. A wooden **rod** is put through the hole. The coins can be rolled from place to place.

_____ **5.** In this story the word **rod** means

        **A.** cannon     **B.** pole        **C.** office

---

The Great Salt Lake is in Utah. It used to be large. But it gets smaller each year. Homes that people built on the shore are now far from the water. This has happened because it is so hot and dry there. The water dries up or **soaks** into the ground. There's not enough fresh water to make up for this loss.

_____ **6.** In this story the word **soaks** means

        **A.** feels      **B.** sinks       **C.** ties

# *Think and Apply*

## Word Search

Each of the sentences on this page is missing a word. Read the sentences. Choose a word from the word box to go in each one. Write the word on the line.

| | | |
|---|---|---|
| stage | envelope | oats |
| arrive | lightning | crayon |

**1.** Beth fed the horse some hay and _____ .

**2.** We clapped when the singer came on _____ .

**3.** Jim used a green _____ to color his picture.

**4.** When will our train _____ in the city?

**5.** A flash of _____ lit up the stormy sky.

**6.** Mail your letter in this _____ .

**To check your answers, turn to page 62.**

## Belonging Together

Use the context to understand the words in **dark letters**. Then circle other words that belong in the same group.

1. A **battery** makes a flashlight work.
   What else uses a **battery**?
   tree              radio
   clock             goat

2. You can **crack** a tooth.
   What else can you **crack**?
   nut               rag
   dish              answer

3. A scratch is a type of **injury**.
   What else is a type of **injury**?
   broken bone       cut
   bent nail         garden

4. You can **measure** how wide your room is.
   What else can you **measure**?
   rice to cook      how tall you are
   eye color         the smell of flowers

5. If you own a car, it is your **property**.
   What other things can be your **property**?
   day               land
   parade            house

To check your answers, turn to page 62.

## Double O in Context

Two *o*'s form a part of many different words. Read the sentences below. One word has been left out of each sentence. Look at where the double *o* is placed in that word. Write letters on the lines to make the correct word.

**1.** A house has many separate ___ oo ___ ___ .

**2.** You can sweep with a ___ ___ oo ___ .

**3.** You can wear ___ oo ___ ___ to protect your feet in rain and snow.

**4.** A horse's foot is a ___ oo ___.

**5.** An animal that jumps and has a pouch is a ___ ___ ___ ___ ___ ___ oo.

**6.** When something happens before very long, it happens ___ oo ___ .

**7.** When you have a cold, you might like to eat some chicken and ___ oo ___ ___ ___ soup.

**8.** When something is not tight, it is ___ oo ___ ___ .

**To check your answers, turn to page 62.**

# ✓ Check Yourself

| Unit 1 pp. 6-7 | Unit 2 pp. 8-9 | Unit 3 pp. 10-11 | Unit 4 pp. 12-13 | Unit 5 pp. 14-15 | Unit 6 pp. 16-17 | Unit 7 pp. 18-19 | Unit 8 pp. 20-21 |
|---|---|---|---|---|---|---|---|
| 1. B | 1. B | 1. A | 1. C | 1. C | 1. B | 1. A | 1. C |
| 2. A | 2. A | 2. C | 2. A | 2. A | 2. A | 2. C | 2. B |
| 3. B | 3. B | 3. B | 3. B | 3. C | 3. B | 3. B | 3. C |
| 4. A | 4. C | 4. B | 4. A | 4. B | 4. C | 4. C | 4. A |
| 5. C | 5. B | 5. B | 5. C | 5. A | 5. C | 5. B | 5. A |
| 6. C | 6. A | 6. A | 6. B | 6. B | 6. A | 6. A | 6. B |

| Unit 9 pp. 22-23 | Unit 10 pp. 24-25 | Unit 11 pp. 26-27 | Unit 12 pp. 28-29 | Unit 13 pp. 30-31 | Unit 14 pp. 32-33 | Unit 15 pp. 34-35 | Unit 16 pp. 36-37 |
|---|---|---|---|---|---|---|---|
| 1. B | 1. A | 1. C | 1. B | 1. A | 1. A | 1. B | 1. C |
| 2. A | 2. C | 2. C | 2. C | 2. B | 2. C | 2. B | 2. B |
| 3. C | 3. A | 3. B | 3. C | 3. C | 3. B | 3. A | 3. C |
| 4. C | 4. B | 4. C | 4. A | 4. C | 4. A | 4. B | 4. A |
| 5. B | 5. A | 5. B | 5. B | 5. B | 5. C | 5. C | 5. B |
| 6. C | 6. B | 6. A | 6. B | 6. A | 6. C | 6. A | 6. A |

| Unit 17 | Unit 18 | Unit 19 | Unit 20 | Unit 21 | Unit 22 | Unit 23 | Unit 24 | Unit 25 |
| pp. 38-39 | pp. 40-41 | pp. 42-43 | pp. 44-45 | pp. 46-47 | pp. 48-49 | pp. 50-51 | pp. 52-53 | pp. 54-55 |
|---|---|---|---|---|---|---|---|---|
| 1. A | 1. B | 1. C | 1. B | 1. A | 1. C | 1. A | 1. B | 1. C |
| 2. B | 2. A | 2. B | 2. B | 2. C | 2. B | 2. B | 2. A | 2. C |
| 3. A | 3. C | 3. C | 3. A | 3. A | 3. A | 3. C | 3. C | 3. A |
| 4. C | 4. C | 4. A | 4. A | 4. B | 4. A | 4. C | 4. B | 4. A |
| 5. C | 5. B | 5. C | 5. C | 5. A | 5. C | 5. A | 5. A | 5. B |
| 6. B | 6. A | 6. A | 6. C | 6. C | 6. A | 6. B | 6. C | 6. B |

**How to Use Context, Page 3**

In the story on page 2, the sentences "You're really good!" and "Go ahead and try to make the big time" should be circled.

Any word that means *to help someone* may be written on the line. Some words with this meaning include *to cheer up*, *to support*, *to back*, and *to help*.

**Working with Context, Page 4**

**1. B**

**2. A**

**Word Search, Page 56**

**1.** oats

**2.** stage

**3.** crayon

**4.** arrive

**5.** lightning

**6.** envelope

**Belonging Together, Page 57**

**1.** clock, radio

**2.** nut, dish

**3.** broken bone, cut

**4.** rice to cook, how tall you are

**5.** land, house

**Double *O* in Context, Page 58**

| | |
|---|---|
| **1.** rooms | **5.** kangaroo |
| **2.** broom | **6.** soon |
| **3.** boots | **7.** noodle |
| **4.** hoof | **8.** loose |